TEN PRELUDES
FOR ORGAN

JOHN ADAMS

kevin mayhew

We hope you enjoy the music in this book.
Further copies of this and our many other books are available
from your local Kevin Mayhew stockist.

In case of difficulty, or to request a catalogue,
please contact the publisher direct by writing to:

The Sales Department
KEVIN MAYHEW LTD
Buxhall
Stowmarket
Suffolk IP14 3BW

Phone 01449 737978
Fax 01449 737834
E-mail info@kevinmayhewltd.com

First published in Great Britain in 2003 by Kevin Mayhew Ltd.

© Copyright 2003 Kevin Mayhew Ltd.

ISBN 1 84417 035 7
ISMN M 57024 171 2
Catalogue No: 1400340

0 1 2 3 4 5 6 7 8 9

Cover design: Angela Selfe
Music setter: Donald Thomson
Proof reader: Kate Gallaher

Printed and bound in Great Britain

Contents

CANON ON 'AURELIA'

John Adams

PRELUDE ON 'DARWALL'S 148TH'

John Adams

a piacere

Sw.　　Gt.

Add Full Sw.
Box closed

poco rall.

cresc.

Tpt.

PRELUDE ON 'HORSLEY'

John Adams

To Nicholas Woods

PRELUDE ON 'HYFRYDOL'

John Adams

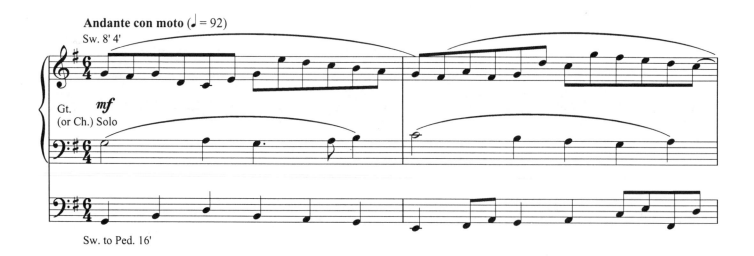

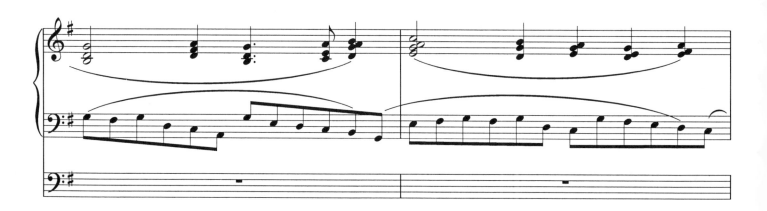

Gt. Ped. off

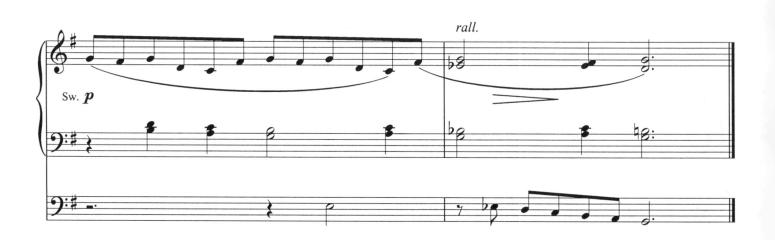

PRELUDE ON 'LOVE DIVINE'

John Adams

To Hazel, with love

PRELUDE ON 'MELITA'

John Adams

MEDITATION ON 'PICARDY'

John Adams

sonore

Sw.

Clarinet Solo

allargando

PRELUDE ON 'RICHMOND'

John Adams

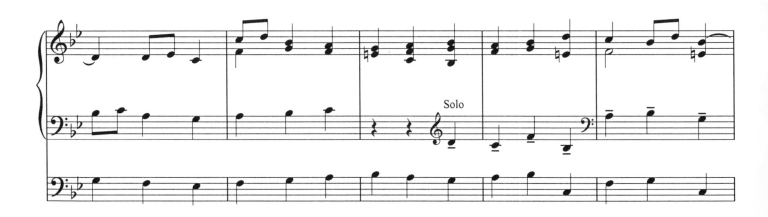

CANON ON 'ST ANNE'

John Adams

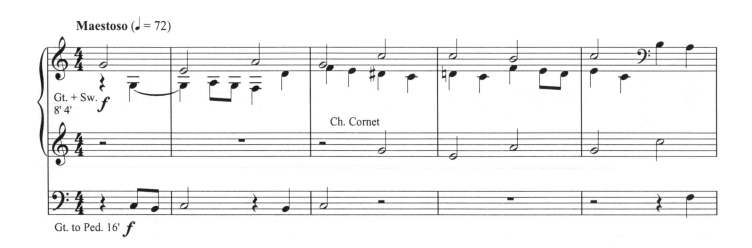

poco rall.

PRELUDE ON 'TRURO'

John Adams

sonore

rall.

Gt. **ff**

Trumpet